This Workbook Belongs To:

_____

In This Workbook

A Note from The Author 1

Seeking Professional Help 2

Mindfulness 3

8 Areas of Wellness 5

Redirecting Thoughts & Focus 21

Cognitive Behavioral Therapy 22

Thought Diary 33

Cognitive Distortions 38

Automatic and Negative Thoughts vs. Affirmations 39

Core Beliefs 44

Recognizing Your Power 50

Control Bubble 51

Challenging Distortions 58

Fact or Fiction 59

Cognitive Reframe 64

Triggers 71

Coping Skills 76

Defense Mechanism 81

Maladaptive Coping Skills 82

The Cognitive Behavioral Cycle 89

Compartmentalizing 95

Self-Care 108

A Note from The Author

It is not uncommon for people to experience low self-esteem and self-worth and feel inadequate and worthlessness. These feelings can result from a negative interaction or can come from within. Low self-esteem and worthlessness are powerful and can paralyze a person from going after a dream and even forfeit one's purpose and full potential.

Although negative thoughts and low self-esteem are powerful, we can defeat them. Over the past seven years as a clinical therapist, I have worked with about 100 children and adults to increase their self-worth, and replace their negative thoughts and behaviors with positive, uplifting, and fulfilling ones. It is difficult, but it is possible, and this workbook can help.

This workbook will challenge your awareness, acceptance, and responsibility, but it will also empower you and build you up.

Seeking Professional Help

You are not an island nor are you alone, even if you feel and believe you are. You are strong, beautiful, intelligent, amazing, and resilient. There is a high probability that you will feel flooded with emotions and thoughts while completing this workbook. If you do not have a therapist, I strongly encourage you to connect with one if you need to go deeper in your healing work after reading and completing this workbook.

Seeking professional help from a licensed clinician does not make you crazy, weak, or incapable of solving your own problems. Talk therapy helps you openly address your concerns and discuss ideas and frustrations. Therapy can help you conceptualize or make sense of your experiences and overall life. Therapy can also help you with decisions and coach you through difficult times. In therapy, you will feel supported, uplifted, validated, and yes, vulnerable.

Disclaimer: Like any other profession, therapists are human, and your relationship and connection matters. Your relationship and compatibility with your therapist are important, so you must find the right one for you.

Mindfulness

Mindfulness is being in the moment. Many of us spend so much time either avoiding our thoughts or being so stuck in our thoughts that we miss many important moments. Mindfulness takes your mind out of the future or the past and brings you to the present.

Mindfulness is good to use because it grounds you. It is a great tool to use against cognitive distortions. Cognitive distortions are supported and reinforced by negative experiences, and mindfulness can bring you back to rational thinking.

Identifying your negative thoughts, distortions, self-esteem, and triggers is not fun and does not feel good. In completing this workbook, you are doing the dirty work necessary to improve your life. There will be times when looking inside yourself is overwhelming, but mindfulness will help you through it. You will find mindful moments of meditation and deep-breathing exercises to help you manage your emotional response.

Mindful Moment

Take a deep breath!

1. Breathe in for <u>four</u> seconds.

2. Hold the breath for <u>four</u> seconds.

3. Breathe out for <u>four</u> seconds.

4. Repeat for at least <u>three</u> deep breaths.

8 Areas of Wellness

-Definitions in quotations are from Northwestern University, Wellness at Northwestern-

Emotional—"*Coping effectively with life and creating satisfying relationships.*" There are many ways to achieve emotional wellness. Seeking counseling for unresolved pain, trauma or for emotional balance, reading books, completing self-help journals, and daily practice are just a few examples.

Spiritual—"*Expanding a sense of purpose and meaning in life.*" Seeking understanding through personal study and experience with your creator/source of hope.

Social—"*Developing a sense of connection, belonging, and a well-developed support system.*" With a balanced level of self-reflections and trust in deserving companions, you can build a great network of reciprocating friends.

Physical—"*Recognizing the need for physical activity, healthy foods, and sleep.*" The level of functioning in your physical body is crucial to the connections between your mind, spirit, and body. Your physical functioning also impacts how well you can manage any other area of wellness and must be in your top three priorities. How you manage your physical body may vary (diet, exercise, etc..), but taking care of yourself physically cannot be an afterthought.

Intellectual—"*Recognizing creative abilities and finding ways to expand knowledge and skills.*" Knowledge is power. Increase your power by learning more about your career field, interests, and hobbies.

Occupational—"*Personal satisfaction and enrichment from one's work.*" If you hate your job, there are ways out. Search within yourself for your true passions and pursue them. So, what if you have to stay at the job you hate until you reach your goal? You are never wasting time if you are making strides in the right direction. Don't despise your small beginnings. To become an oak tree, you have to endure the lifespan of the acorn.

Financial—"*Satisfaction with current and future financial situations.*" Financial wellness is not only about what's coming in but also what's going out. Financial wellness may include learning to make responsible and healthy financial choices.

Environmental—"*Good health by occupying pleasant, stimulating environments that support well-being.*" Your environment has the power to directly impact your mood and productivity. If you are an adult, you have ultimate control over your environment. It may take time and effort to create the environment that works best for you, but it will be worth it.

When we prioritize the eight areas of wellness in life, we can achieve complete wellness.

On a scale from 0 to 5, with 0 being not at all and 5 being very much, rate how well you prioritize the following areas:

Emotional—Coping effectively with life and creating satisfying relationships.

0   1   2   3   4   5

Spiritual—Expanding a sense of purpose and meaning in life.

0   1   2   3   4   5

Social—Developing a sense of connection, belonging, and a well-developed support system.

0   1   2   3   4   5

Physical—Recognizing the need for physical activity, healthy foods, and sleep.

0   1   2   3   4   5

Intellectual—Recognizing creative abilities and finding ways to expand knowledge and skills.

0   1   2   3   4   5

Occupational—Personal satisfaction and enrichment from one's work.

0   1   2   3   4   5

Environmental—Good health by occupying pleasant, stimulating environments that support well-being.

0   1   2   3   4   5

Financial—Satisfaction with current and future financial situations.

0   1   2   3   4   5

It is important that we work towards improving our wellness. Create a wellness plan to help you achieve this goal. List at least one thing you can do to improve your current level of functioning. List the steps you will take and add a due date to hold yourself accountable.

Emotional Wellness Plan:

_____
_____
_____
_____
_____
_____
_____
_____
_____
_____

Action Steps:

_____
_____
_____
_____
_____
_____

Due Date: _____

Spiritual Wellness Plan:

_____

_____

_____

_____

_____

_____

_____

_____

_____

_____

_____

Action Steps:

_____

_____

_____

_____

_____

_____

_____

Due Date: _____

Social Wellness Plan:

_____

_____

_____

_____

_____

_____

_____

_____

_____

_____

_____

Action Steps:

_____

_____

_____

_____

_____

_____

_____

Due Date: _____

Physical Wellness Plan:

_____

_____

_____

_____

_____

_____

_____

_____

_____

_____

_____

_____

Action Steps:

_____

_____

_____

_____

_____

_____

_____

Due Date: _____

Intellectual Wellness Plan:

_____

_____

_____

_____

_____

_____

_____

_____

_____

_____

_____

_____

Action Steps:

_____

_____

_____

_____

_____

_____

_____

Due Date: _____

Occupational Wellness Plan:

_____

_____

_____

_____

_____

_____

_____

_____

_____

_____

Action Steps:

_____

_____

_____

_____

_____

_____

_____

Due Date: _____

Financial Wellness Plan:

_____

_____

_____

_____

_____

_____

_____

_____

_____

_____

_____

_____

Action Steps:

_____

_____

_____

_____

_____

_____

_____

Due Date: _____

Environmental Wellness Plan:

_____

_____

_____

_____

_____

_____

_____

_____

_____

_____

Action Steps:

_____

_____

_____

_____

_____

_____

_____

Due Date: _____

Mindful Moment

Take a deep breath!

1. Breathe in for <u>four</u> seconds

2. Hold the breath for <u>four</u> seconds

3. Breathe out for <u>four</u> seconds.

4. Repeat for at least <u>three</u> deep breaths.

Let's begin with evaluating your starting point. Don't get upset by low scores. You will evaluate yourself later and will see how much you have improved.

On a scale of 0 to 5, with 0 being not at all and 5 being very much, rate how you feel right now in the following categories:

Confident

0   1   2   3   4   5

Happy

0   1   2   3   4   5

Sad

0   1   2   3   4   5

Disgusted

0   1   2   3   4   5

Overwhelmed

0   1   2   3   4   5

Alone

0   1   2   3   4   5

Loved

0   1   2   3   4   5

Liked

0   1   2   3   4   5

Attractive

0   1   2   3   4   5

Depressed

0   1   2   3   4   5

Anxious

0   1   2   3   4   5

Healthy

0   1   2   3   4   5

Satisfied

0   1   2   3   4   5

Fulfilled

0   1   2   3   4   5

Write about your experience with today's activity. What did you learn about yourself? What do you need to work on? What thoughts and emotions were triggered by the activity? What can you do to make positive changes?

_____

_____

_____

_____

_____

_____

_____

_____

_____

_____

_____

_____

_____

_____

_____

_____

_____

_____

_____

_____

_____

_____

_____

_____

Mindful Moment

Take a deep breath!

1. Sit up straight and place your hand on your belly.

2. Breathe in for <u>four</u> seconds. Focus on your belly as you inhale.

3. Hold the breath for <u>four</u> seconds

4. Breathe out for <u>four</u> seconds. Slowly push out all the air in your lungs.

5. Repeat for at least <u>three</u> deep breaths.

Redirecting Thoughts & Focus

Thinking positively when deep down you don't believe it is hard, but it is necessary. Let's say a person is not happy about their job and every day they get up dreading going to work, thinking of all the bad that will most likely happen and all the reasons they want to quit. Do you think they got to that point after one bad day? No, they most likely have a consistent stream of thoughts that are constantly reinforced.

What if they changed the direction of their thoughts? What if they began the day with, "Today I'm grateful to have a job"? What if they repeated this positive phrase each time they became triggered? How do you think this thought would affect their day? It would not take away the triggers on the job, but it would change the emotional response and mood. If you have a negative outlook, it may seem that there is no way out or a solution to a problem. A positive perspective will create an opportunity for positive change. A negative mindset says, "I can't do it." A positive mindset says, "I can do it," or "How can I do it?"

Your thoughts are a road map and you can reroute yourself in more positive and affirming directions.

Cognitive Behavioral Therapy

Cognitive Behavioral Therapy (CBT) is a therapy model that focuses on the connection between one's thoughts and behaviors. Our thoughts and feelings are directly connected to our behavior. If we think we are inadequate, then we will behave and act out those inadequacies. This can be done overtly (ex: refusing to apply for a job because we don't think we are qualified) or these behaviors can be subconscious and without immediate awareness that they are happening (ex: never considering applying for a job because you don't consider your qualifications.)

I've worked with people who thought so poorly of themselves that they did not believe they deserved anything, not even a shower. Once we began working to change their thoughts and beliefs, they began to treat themselves with more respect and they improved their hygiene and other negative behaviors, but it all started with their thoughts.

In this workbook, we will identify the negative thoughts and feelings you have about yourself with the expectation that you will then change your behavior.

How do you describe yourself? In the columns below, write down the positive and negative traits you see in yourself.

Positive Traits   Negative Traits

_____   _____

_____   _____

_____   _____

_____   _____

_____   _____

_____   _____

_____   _____

_____   _____

_____   _____

_____   _____

_____   _____

_____   _____

_____   _____

_____   _____

_____   _____

_____   _____

_____   _____

_____   _____

_____   _____

_____   _____

_____   _____

_____   _____

Think about the negative traits you listed. Where did they come from and when did they start? Do you want to eliminate negative traits and behaviors? What changes do you need to make?

_____

_____

_____

_____

_____

_____

_____

_____

_____

_____

_____

_____

_____

_____

_____

_____

_____

_____

_____

_____

_____

_____

_____

_____

Mindful Moment

Read the following statement out loud:

I deserve love, happiness, and peace. If I don't believe it now, it's okay. I won't stop working towards the truth of this statement. I am more than what I say I am. I am more than what others think of me. I can exceed my wildest dreams.

The list below consists of positive personality traits. Check the box of the traits that you have and place a star next to the traits that you would like to have.

- ❏ Accountable
- ❏ Adaptable
- ❏ Adventurous
- ❏ Affectionate
- ❏ Alert
- ❏ Ambitious
- ❏ Appropriate
- ❏ Assertive
- ❏ Astute
- ❏ Attentive
- ❏ Authentic
- ❏ Aware
- ❏ Brave
- ❏ Calm
- ❏ Candid
- ❏ Capable
- ❏ Certain
- ❏ Charismatic
- ❏ Collaborative
- ❏ Committed
- ❏ Communicator
- ❏ Compassionate
- ❏ Connected
- ❏ Considerate
- ❏ Consistent
- ❏ Cooperative
- ❏ Courageous
- ❏ Creative
- ❏ Curious
- ❏ Dedicated
- ❏ Determined
- ❏ Diplomatic
- ❏ Directive
- ❏ Discipline
- ❏ Easygoing
- ❏ Effective
- ❏ Efficient

- ❏ Empathetic
- ❏ Empowered
- ❏ Energetic
- ❏ Enthusiastic
- ❏ Ethical
- ❏ Excited
- ❏ Expressive
- ❏ Fair
- ❏ Faithful
- ❏ Fearless
- ❏ Flexible
- ❏ Friendly
- ❏ Generous
- ❏ Grateful
- ❏ Happy
- ❏ Hard Working
- ❏ Honest
- ❏ Honorable
- ❏ Humorous
- ❏ Imaginative
- ❏ Immaculate
- ❏ Independent
- ❏ Innovative
- ❏ Inquiring
- ❏ Integrity
- ❏ Intelligent
- ❏ Intentional
- ❏ Interested
- ❏ Joyful
- ❏ Knowledgeable
- ❏ Listener
- ❏ Lively
- ❏ Logical
- ❏ Loving
- ❏ Loyal
- ❏ Manages Time Well
- ❏ Networker

- ❏ Nurturing
- ❏ Open-Minded
- ❏ Optimistic
- ❏ Organized
- ❏ Patient
- ❏ Peaceful
- ❏ Planner
- ❏ Playful
- ❏ Poised
- ❏ Polite
- ❏ Powerful
- ❏ Practical
- ❏ Presents Self Well
- ❏ Proactive
- ❏ Problem-Solver
- ❏ Productive
- ❏ Punctual
- ❏ Reliable
- ❏ Resourceful
- ❏ Responsible
- ❏ Self-confident

- ❏ Self-reliant
- ❏ Sensual
- ❏ Serves Others
- ❏ Sincere
- ❏ Skillful
- ❏ Spiritual
- ❏ Spontaneous
- ❏ Stable
- ❏ Strong
- ❏ Successful
- ❏ Supportive
- ❏ Tactful
- ❏ Trusting
- ❏ Trustworthy
- ❏ Truthful
- ❏ Versatile
- ❏ Vibrant
- ❏ Warm
- ❏ Willing
- ❏ Wise
- ❏ Zealous

List the traits you starred below to complete the "I Am" statements. These completed statements will serve as your positive affirmations. Positive affirmations are statements, phrases, or quotes used to uplift and encourage.

Recite these statements every time you have a negative thought. When reciting positive affirmations, it is not uncommon to feel silly or as if you are lying. Negativity is rehearsed daily, so you will need to recite these positive affirmations daily to accept, believe, and then feel empowered by them.

I am _____   I am _____

I am _____   I am _____

I am _____   I am _____

I am _____   I am _____

I am _____   I am _____

I am _____   I am _____

I am _____   I am _____

I am _____   I am _____

I am _____   I am _____

I am _____   I am _____

I am _____   I am _____

I am _____   I am _____

I am _____   I am _____

I am _____   I am _____

I am _____   I am _____

I am _____   I am _____

I am _____   I am _____

I am _____   I am _____

Write about your experience with today's activity. How did you feel writing and reciting the "I Am" statements? What thoughts and emotions were triggered by the activity? Did it feel as though you were lying to yourself?

Mindful Moment

Gratitude Challenge:

It is easy to focus only on the negative. Take some time and list five things/reasons you have to be grateful. Here is one reason to start: **You are alive, and with every new day, you have the opportunity to make major positive changes in your life.**

1.

2.

3.

4.

5.

Thought Diary

How many positive or negative thoughts do you have throughout the day? For the next 12 hours, keep track of your thoughts and add a check under positive if it is a good thought or under negative if it is a bad thought.

Thoughts   Positive   Negative

Thoughts   **Positive**   **Negative**

How many positive and negative thoughts did you have? How did the thoughts impact your day? Are you aware of what caused or triggered the thoughts? Write about the experience below.

_____

_____

_____

_____

_____

_____

_____

_____

_____

_____

_____

_____

_____

_____

_____

_____

_____

_____

_____

_____

_____

_____

_____

_____

_____

Mindful Moment

Use your five senses to focus and stay present in this moment. What is happening right here and now?

Sight: Look around and find five items that are the same color.

Touch: Touch four items around you, each having a different texture.

Hearing: Listen and identify three different sounds that you hear.

Smell: Smell two different scents.

Taste: Eat something sweet and something salty (if available) and notice the distinct differences in taste.

Cognitive Distortions

A cognitive distortion is a negative way of thinking about something. The thought, "Nobody likes me," is an example of a cognitive distortion. It overgeneralizes and discounts the many people that do like and even love you.

There are many other types of cognitive distortions: overgeneralizing, blaming, catastrophizing, magnifying, mind-reading, emotional reasoning and more, but for the sake of this workbook, cognitive distortions are any automatic, negative, and exaggerated thoughts that hold you back from fully loving yourself and/or others. Usually, these thoughts are only based on your experience and from your perspective.

Automatic and Negative Thoughts vs. Affirmations

Have you ever gotten dressed up and still did not feel pretty because someone told you that you are ugly? Has someone ever pointed out one of your flaws and no matter what you do to improve it, you still see that flaw? Have you picked out every possible thing wrong with you? Do those thoughts plague your mind daily? Do the negative words play like a recording in your mind? These repetitive and/or automatic thoughts often cause lack of progress, motivation, self-consciousness, fear, and doubt.

These negative thoughts greatly increase the negative impact on your mood and behavior. If we replace negative thoughts with positive statements and affirmations, then we can create an appropriate mindset and environment for positive mood and behavior changes.

In the first column, write down every negative thought you believe others think about you and what you think of yourself. In the second column, write down the opposite of each thought you wrote in the first column. The second column will serve as another list of positive affirmations to recite daily.

For example: Column 1 "No one likes me." vs. Column 2 "People like me."

Column 1   Column 2

_____   _____

_____   _____

_____   _____

_____   _____

_____   _____

_____   _____

_____   _____

_____   _____

_____   _____

_____   _____

_____   _____

_____   _____

_____   _____

_____   _____

_____   _____

_____   _____

Write about your experience with today's activity. Did you have many negative thoughts? What emotions were triggered by the activity and why?

_____

_____

_____

_____

_____

_____

_____

_____

_____

_____

_____

_____

_____

_____

_____

_____

_____

_____

_____

_____

_____

_____

_____

_____

_____

_____

_____

_____

Mindful Moment

Read all the instructions below before beginning the activity.

1. Breathe slow and deep.

2. At the same time, close your eyes and think of the color yellow.

3. Hold the color in your mind for one inhale and one exhale.

4. Think of three items that are yellow. For example, a school bus, sunflower, and a bee.

5. Repeat this activity with the colors blue, green and red.

Core Beliefs

In addition to automatic thoughts, we have core beliefs. A belief is a thought that you have made real in your life. Thoughts can fire rapidly in your mind and be both positive and negative. A belief is a thought that has lingered long enough to stick. People act on both thoughts and beliefs since both have the power to impact behavior.

A core belief is what we feel about ourselves, others, and the world. Core beliefs also shape our behavior. If our core beliefs are irrational or unhealthy, then our behaviors will also be irrational and unhealthy. Here are some examples:

Core belief of self: "I'm a good person."

Core belief of others: "People are not safe, don't let them in."

Core belief of the world: "The world is not safe."

List your core beliefs below:

Belief of Self:

_____

_____

_____

_____

_____

_____

_____

Belief of Others:

_____

_____

_____

_____

_____

_____

_____

Belief of the World:

_____

_____

_____

_____

_____

_____

_____

If you recognize any of your core beliefs as negative, irrational, or limiting, write the opposing statement of your core beliefs below. For example, "The world is bad," would become, "The world is not all bad."

Belief of Self:

_____
_____
_____
_____
_____
_____
_____

Belief of Others:

_____
_____
_____
_____
_____
_____
_____

Belief of the World:

_____
_____
_____
_____
_____
_____
_____

Write about your experience with today's activity. Are you shocked or surprised by some of your core beliefs now that you see them in writing?

Do you recognize any of them as cognitive distortions or based on irrational thinking? What thoughts and emotions were triggered by the activity?

_____

_____

_____

_____

_____

_____

_____

_____

_____

_____

_____

_____

_____

_____

_____

_____

_____

_____

_____

_____

_____

_____

_____

_____

_____

_____

Date: _____

Mindful Moment

Take a deep breath!

1. Sit up straight and place your hand on your belly.

2. Breathe in for <u>four</u> seconds. Focus on your belly as you inhale.

3. Hold the breath for <u>four</u> seconds.

4. Breathe out for <u>four</u> seconds. Slowly push out all the air in your lungs.

5. Repeat at least <u>three</u> deep breaths.

Recognizing Your Power

You have the power to control your thoughts, your behavior, and your life. I usually like to illustrate this point by using two bubbles, one large bubble and one medium bubble. The large bubble represents all the things in life that you cannot directly control. Inside the large bubble would be other people, including but not limited to their thoughts, behaviors, opinions, emotional state, rules, etc. Inside the medium bubble would be everything you can directly control, including but not limited to your thoughts, behaviors, what you say, your beliefs, reactions, decisions, goals, progress, etc.

Many people spend more time and energy trying to manage the things outside of their realm of control while neglecting the things directly in their control.

Other people can't easily control us when we recognize our power. That is not to say you can't be influenced by others, but keep in mind that to be influenced, you have to allow it, meaning that you are still in control.

Control Bubble

List whatever you can think of that is directly in your control. Add to the list of things outside of your control. As you go throughout your day, focus solely on things that you can control.

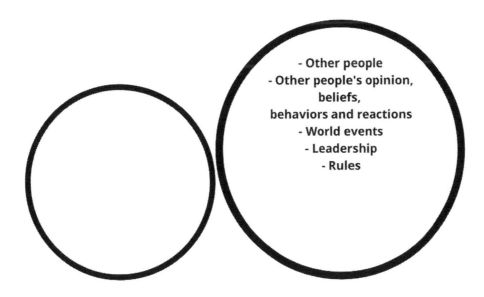

- Other people
- Other people's opinion, beliefs,
behaviors and reactions
- World events
- Leadership
- Rules

Did you notice that your bubble of control is much smaller than the bubble of things that you can't control? How do you feel about that? Write about your experience operating in your bubble of control.

_____

_____

_____

_____

_____

_____

_____

_____

_____

_____

_____

_____

_____

_____

_____

_____

_____

_____

_____

_____

_____

_____

_____

_____

_____

Mindful Moment

Stretch

1. Stand up tall with your hands by your side.

2. Stretch your head from left to right and hold for five seconds on each side.

3. Slowly roll your head three times in both directions.

4. Stretch your arms towards the sky, look up, and hold for 10 seconds.

5. Bend down, touch your toes, and hold for 10 seconds.

Recite all the affirmations you've created from the "I Am" statements and the opposing statements from your list of negative thoughts and core beliefs out loud. What did you experience while reciting the affirmations? What thoughts and emotions were triggered by the activity? Did it feel as though you were lying to yourself?

_____

_____

_____

_____

_____

_____

_____

_____

_____

_____

_____

_____

_____

_____

_____

_____

_____

_____

_____

_____

_____

_____

_____

_____

Mindful Moment

Read the following statement out loud:

I deserve love, happiness, and peace. If I don't believe it now, it's okay. I won't stop working towards the truth of this statement. I am more than what I say I am. I am more than what others think of me. I can exceed my wildest dreams.

Challenging Distortions

We challenge cognitive distortions by shining a light on them. Awareness is key, and knowledge is power. When you know a person's game, they cannot win against you. Cognitive distortions are the enemy and once you know their tactics, you can defeat them.

When you challenge your cognitive distortions, you may feel you are challenging yourself in many ways. Essentially, you are; you are challenging yourself to be better, braver, and stronger than you are now. Much like exercising the physical body, you don't make major changes after one workout. Consistent workouts, a healthy diet, and a positive mindset make all the difference. This workbook will teach you a few ways to challenge your cognitive distortions.

Fact or Fiction challenges your thoughts against any supporting or disproving evidence. Thought stopping/swapping challenges your active thoughts and replaces them with more positive and appropriate thoughts. Reflection provides the opportunity to review, evaluate, and adjust thoughts and behaviors.

Fact or Fiction

Cognitive distortions are usually fed by irrational and exaggerated sub-thoughts. Read the negative thoughts column from the previous activity. Do you have any proof that what you wrote down is true, or are they thoughts that you made true in your mind?

For example, if your negative thought is an overgeneralized thought such as, "Everyone hates me," but you can name people who love you, then that negative thought would be considered fiction.

Go through your list of automatic/negative thoughts. List the supporting or disproving evidence for each negative thought in correct columns under fact or fiction.

Fact   Fiction

_____   _____

_____   _____

_____   _____

_____   _____

_____   _____

_____   _____

_____   _____

_____   _____

_____   _____

_____   _____

_____   _____

_____   _____

_____   _____

_____   _____

_____   _____

_____   _____

Write about your experience with today's activity. Did you find that some of your thoughts are fiction? How do you feel knowing that some of your frequent thoughts are not based in fact? What thoughts and emotions were triggered by the activity?

_____

_____

_____

_____

_____

_____

_____

_____

_____

_____

_____

_____

_____

_____

_____

_____

_____

_____

_____

_____

_____

_____

_____

_____

Mindful Moment

Read all the instructions below before beginning the activity.

1. Breathe slow and deep.

2. At the same time, close your eyes and think of the color yellow.

3. Hold the color in your mind for one inhale and one exhale.

4. Think of three items that are yellow. For example, a school bus, sunflower, and a bee.

5. Repeat this activity with the colors blue, green and red.

Cognitive Reframe

Imagine accidentally knocking over a picture frame holding a picture of you and your best friend. If you break the frame, you will probably want to go out and purchase a new frame right away. You will take the picture from the broken frame and put it in a new frame. This is how cognitive reframing works. Cognitive reframe is when you take one thought and reshape or reframe it into a more positive thought or look at it from a positive point of view.

During the Covid-19 (Coronavirus) pandemic of 2020, many of us struggled to manage our mood because of the constant influx of bad news, misinformation, and the death tolls.

Some negative thoughts and statements I had and heard were: "I can't believe I have to stay home!" "I want to go out, I hate working from home." "What? They are canceling schools?!"

The cognitive reframe or (positive reframe) for these previous statements would be: "I am safe when I'm home." "I still have a job and the ability to work in the safety of my home." "Kids are safer at home and can learn in the safety of their homes."

Cognitively reframing our statements does not immediately change the frustrations and difficulty we face, but it can minimize our emotional and behavioral responses when we are triggered. Cognitive reframe will help us look at our situations with a new lens.

What are some of the negative thoughts and statements that you've made about your life, relationships, financial status, and career, etc.?

Write them down and then re-write them using cognitive reframe (a more positive perspective).

_____

_____

_____

_____

_____

_____

_____

_____

_____

_____

_____

_____

_____

_____

_____

_____

_____

_____

_____

_____

_____

_____

_____

_____

_____

Mindful Moment

Stretch

1. Stand up tall with your hands by your side.

2. Stretch your head from left to right and hold for five seconds on each side.

3. Slowly roll your head three times in both directions.

4. Stretch your arms towards the sky, look up, and hold for 10 seconds.

5. Bend down, touch your toes, and hold for 10 seconds.

Recite all the affirmations you've created from the "I Am" statements and the opposing statements from your list of negative thoughts and core beliefs out loud. What did you experience while reciting the affirmations? What thoughts and emotions were triggered by the activity? Did it feel as though you were lying to yourself?

_____

_____

_____

_____

_____

_____

_____

_____

_____

_____

_____

_____

_____

_____

_____

_____

_____

_____

_____

_____

_____

_____

_____

Mindful Moment

Take a deep breath!

1. Breathe in for <u>four</u> seconds

2. Hold the breath for <u>four</u> seconds

3. Breathe out for <u>four</u> seconds.

4. Repeat for at least <u>three</u> deep breaths.

Triggers

Understanding, maintaining, or taking back your power can be achieved when you know what triggers your emotional responses and behaviors.

Triggers can be positive or negative. If you baked cakes or pies with your mother growing up, you may be flooded with positive memories any time you smell a freshly baked cake or pie. If you grew up hearing a lot of yelling and fighting as a kid, you may be triggered with negative memories when you hear loud noises.

Managing negative triggers helps with your emotional and behavioral response. Watching a sad movie can make you cry, but you can also turn it off or decide in advance not to watch it. That is using your power. If you watch the sad movie and you become triggered to cry or feel sad, you can use your power by doing or thinking of something that usually makes you happy to combat or change the sad mood. That is an example of a coping skill.

In order to stop the negative thoughts that feed low self-esteem, it's important to know what triggers those thoughts. What happens right before you begin to feel bad about yourself?

For example, if you pick yourself apart while getting dressed to go into a public setting, the trigger could be going into public, getting dressed up, looking in the mirror, negative comments from other people, etc.

List your triggers below.

_____	_____
_____	_____
_____	_____

Write about your experience with today's activity. Were you aware of all of the triggers you listed? What thoughts and emotions were triggered by the activity?

_____

_____

_____

_____

_____

_____

_____

_____

_____

_____

_____

_____

_____

_____

_____

_____

_____

_____

_____

_____

_____

_____

_____

_____

_____

Mindful Moment

Body Scan

Read instructions all the way through before starting activity.

1. Set a timer for one minute.

2. Sit up straight or lie flat on the floor.

3. Quiet your mind.

4. Start at the top of your head and focus on relaxing your head.

5. Slowly work your way down, relaxing each part of your body (neck, shoulders, torso, pelvis, legs, and feet).

6. If you finish before the timer, lie still, and relax.

Coping Skills

A coping skill or mechanism is an activity used to manage, cope, or regulate one's thoughts, mood, or behaviors. For low moods, find an uplifting activity, and for an anxious or angry mood, find a calming or de-escalating activity. Some deescalating activities may require a physical release of energy such as exercising, yelling, or hitting something (it is not recommended to hit a person or animal).

Coping skills are relative to individual interest and it's important to have a toolbox of several coping skills to use at various times. The impact of each skill may vary based on the trigger. Identify and practice your coping skills so they become second nature for you to use when triggered.

Here are a few coping skills to choose from. Put a check mark by the skills that you plan to use. Write in any additional skills that you want to implement.

- ❏ Journal thoughts
- ❏ Paint
- ❏ Draw
- ❏ Cook/Bake
- ❏ Talk to someone you can trust
- ❏ Exercise
- ❏ Go for a walk/run
- ❏ Eat a snack
- ❏ Listen to music that will elicit the mood you desire
- ❏ Dance
- ❏ Sing
- ❏ Paint your nails
- ❏ Take bath or shower
- ❏ Knit/Crochet
- ❏ Do your hair
- ❏ Shop (set appropriate boundaries)
- ❏ Eat a snack (set appropriate boundaries)
- ❏ Read
- ❏ Watch a movie
- ❏ Visit a friend
- ❏ Blow bubbles

- ❏ Take deep breaths
- ❏ Scribble/doodle
- ❏ Word Search/Crossword puzzle
- ❏ Cry
- ❏ Yell
- ❏ Punch a pillow/punching bag
- ❏ Play with a pet
- ❏ Take a nap (if you're feeling tired)
- ❏ Meditate
- ❏ Aromatherapy
- ❏ Pedicure
- ❏ Massage
- ❏ Clean/Organize
- ❏ Rip paper into small pieces
- ❏ Facial
- ❏ Set a timer for 15 minutes before reacting, if still upset set it for another 15 minutes.
- ❏ Write down 5 things you're grateful for
- ❏ _____
- ❏ _____
- ❏ _____

How do you plan to use your coping skills? Connect the coping skills with the triggers you listed in the last entry.

_____

_____

_____

_____

_____

_____

_____

_____

_____

_____

_____

_____

_____

_____

_____

_____

_____

_____

_____

_____

_____

_____

_____

_____

_____

_____

Mindful Moment

Take a deep breath!

1. Breathe in for <u>four</u> seconds

2. Hold the breath for <u>four</u> seconds

3. Breathe out for <u>four</u> seconds.

4. Repeat for at least <u>three</u> deep breaths.

Defense Mechanism

Similar to how white blood cells are our body's physical defense, we have many emotional defenses such as avoidance, blaming, projecting, denial, regression and more that protect us from emotional pain.

That doesn't sound like a bad thing, right? Wrong. Defense mechanisms appear to protect us, but they usually prolong us from processing through and moving past a situation. Being vulnerable can be hard, but if we don't open ourselves up when seeking help and healing, we are only putting Band-aids on a hemorrhaging wound.

At times, defense mechanisms can be the only way a person can function in life without totally falling apart. This may be due to experiencing and not processing through trauma. If this is your case, I strongly suggest working on this under the care of your therapist.

Maladaptive Coping Skills

Maladaptive coping skills usually coexist with defense mechanisms. Maladaptive coping skills are unhelpful or negative behaviors to cope with triggers. They may give immediate gratification but do not result in a positive change in mood or rational thinking to address the trigger. While I was a drug and alcohol counselor, many clients shared that they used drugs to cover up and avoid the pain they felt on a daily basis. Although the source of pain for each person varied, the avoidance behavior and maladaptive coping skills were the same. Some maladaptive coping skills include drinking or drug use to numb pain, cutting or other self-harm behaviors, isolation, promiscuous and risky behaviors, avoidance behaviors, and more.

List the defense mechanisms and maladaptive coping skills that you have used and what emotional experience you were trying to avoid. List positive coping skills that can replace your maladaptive behaviors?

_____

_____

_____

_____

_____

_____

_____

_____

_____

_____

_____

_____

_____

_____

_____

_____

_____

_____

_____

_____

_____

_____

_____

_____

_____

_____

Mindful Moment

Stretch

1. Stand up tall with your hands by your side.

2. Stretch your head from left to right and hold for five seconds on each side.

3. Slowly roll your head three times in both directions.

4. Stretch your arms towards the sky, look up, and hold for 10 seconds.

5. Bend down, touch your toes, and hold for 10 seconds.

Recite out loud all the affirmations you've created from the "I Am" statements and the opposing statements from your list of negative thoughts and core beliefs. What did you experience while reciting the affirmations? What thoughts and emotions were triggered by the activity? Did it feel as though you were lying to yourself?

_____

_____

_____

_____

_____

_____

_____

_____

_____

_____

_____

_____

_____

_____

_____

_____

_____

_____

_____

_____

_____

_____

_____

_____

_____

Mindful Moment

Gratitude Challenge:

It is easy to focus only on the negative. Take some time and list five things/reasons you have to be grateful. Here is one reason to start: **You are alive, and with every new day, you have the opportunity to make major positive changes in your life.**

1.

2.

3.

4.

5.

The Cognitive Behavioral Cycle

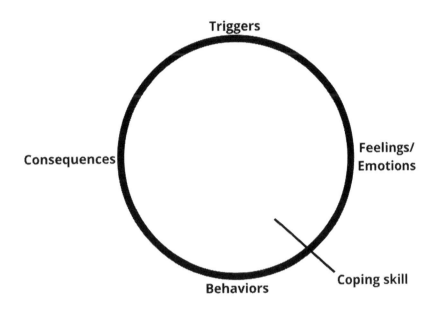

Some emotional responses can lead to long-term and unfortunate consequences. To avoid emotional or inappropriate behaviors, we must break the cycle by implementing coping skills between the emotional experience and the action. For example, if you are arguing with a close friend or spouse (trigger) and become angry (emotional experience) you can make hurtful and damaging statements (behavior) which will either damage or end the relationship (consequence).

You can tell your friend or spouse that you are upset and you need time to calm down (coping skills/positive communication of needs) and then finish the discussion in a better state of mind and with rational thinking. Implementing coping skills prevents the negative behavior and ultimately the negative consequence.

Your actions are a result of your thoughts and beliefs. What are some things you have done (both positive and negative) as a result of your beliefs and thoughts? What can you do differently in the future?

_____

_____

_____

_____

_____

_____

_____

_____

_____

_____

_____

_____

_____

_____

_____

_____

_____

_____

_____

_____

_____

_____

_____

_____

_____

_____

What consequences have your actions had on your self-esteem, life, and overall happiness? Were the actions worth the consequence?

_____

_____

_____

_____

_____

_____

_____

_____

_____

_____

_____

_____

_____

_____

_____

_____

_____

_____

_____

_____

_____

_____

_____

_____

Mindful Moment

Stay in the moment by listening to your favorite song. Listen to the singing and focus on the words.

Compartmentalizing

To compartmentalize means to divide into sections. In terms of our thoughts and beliefs, let's take this definition further.

Compartmentalizing is separating thoughts and placing unhelpful and unproductive thoughts on the shelf until a more appropriate time. Have you ever heard the phrase, "Leave your attitude at the door," or "Don't bring your personal problems to work"? These phrases suggest that you compartmentalize.

Being a licensed therapist does not take away my human nature. If I have an argument with my husband or become triggered by grief, I have to manage my mood appropriately so that my personal emotions don't interfere with my professional work. This in no way implies that feelings should be ignored, but instead should be managed at the appropriate time. If I'm triggered on the way to work, I do my best to reflect, process, and release the triggers and emotional experiences.

Then, I put the entire situation on my imaginary shelf and leave it there so I can do my job effectively. After I do my job and when the time is appropriate, I pick it back up and handle the situation. The time between the triggering event and picking it up from the shelf usually allows enough time to de-escalate (cool down) and increases rational thought to help address the trigger more appropriately. Compartmentalizing also increases productivity when your mind is not focused on your triggers or weighed down by negative emotions.

To summarize, there is a time and place for everything and compartmentalizing allows us to manage our triggers, moods, and behaviors while also maintaining an appropriate level of functioning while at school and work.

Write about ways to compartmentalize your current thoughts and feelings. What do you need to put on your imaginary shelf in order to function at school or work? How can you compartmentalize your low self-esteem or negative thoughts in order to pursue a goal or complete a task?

_____

_____

_____

_____

_____

_____

_____

_____

_____

_____

_____

_____

_____

_____

_____

_____

_____

_____

_____

_____

_____

_____

_____

_____

_____

Mindful Moment

Take a deep breath!

1. Sit up straight and place your hand on your belly.

2. Breathe in for <u>four</u> seconds. Focus on your belly as you inhale.

3. Hold the breath for <u>four</u> seconds.

4. Breathe out for <u>four</u> seconds. Slowly push out all the air in your lungs.

5. Repeat at least <u>three</u> deep breaths.

Write one compliment to yourself and two reasons why you love yourself. Write about the experience, and any difficulty you had. Include all the emotions you experienced.

_____

_____

_____

_____

_____

_____

_____

_____

_____

_____

_____

_____

_____

_____

_____

_____

_____

_____

_____

_____

_____

_____

_____

_____

_____

_____

Mindful Moment

Use your five senses to focus and stay present in this moment. What is happening right here and now?

<u>**Sight**</u>: Look around and find five items that are the same color.

<u>**Touch**</u>: Touch four items around you, each with a different texture.

<u>**Hearing**</u>: Listen and identify three different sounds that you hear.

<u>**Smell**</u>: Smell two different scents.

<u>**Taste**</u>: Eat something sweet and something salty (if available) and notice the distinct differences in taste.

Who do you talk to when you are having negative thoughts and/or feelings? Do you have a support system, friends, or family members you can turn to? If so, write an entry about that person detailing who they are, how you know them, and why you trust them in your time of need.

If you do not have a person, write down the type of person you would like to talk to in your time of need.

_____

_____

_____

_____

_____

_____

_____

_____

_____

_____

_____

_____

_____

_____

_____

_____

_____

_____

_____

_____

_____

_____

_____

Mindful Moment

Stretch

1. Stand up tall with your hands by your side.

2. Stretch your head from left to right and hold for five seconds on each side.

3. Slowly roll your head three times in both directions.

4. Stretch your arms towards the sky, look up, and hold for 10 seconds.

5. Bend down, touch your toes, and hold for 10 seconds.

Recite all the affirmations you've created from the "I Am" statements and the opposing statements from your list of negative thoughts and core beliefs out loud.

What did you experience while reciting the affirmations? What thoughts and emotions were triggered by the activity? Did it feel as though you were lying to yourself?

_____

_____

_____

_____

_____

_____

_____

_____

_____

_____

_____

_____

_____

_____

_____

_____

_____

_____

_____

_____

_____

_____

_____

Mindful Moment

Stay in the moment by listening to your favorite song. Listen to the singing and focus on the words.

Self-Care

Being aware of your triggers is important, but triggers are not always preventable. Our power lies in how we allow ourselves to respond to the triggers and what we do to combat the impact of the triggers. Emotional responses and some thoughts are automatic; if someone steps on your foot, you will feel the pain. However, you have control over whether you punch that person or hold a grudge for the rest of your life. A person has power over you when you allow them to control your emotional responses.

The fact that you are completing this workbook shows your commitment to bettering and caring for yourself and prioritizing your wellness.

Whether you are single or married with children, finding time to focus on yourself can be a challenge. The more you have on your plate, the harder it is. But it is possible and is necessary to prioritize your wellness. You do not have to have weekly spa days and girls' nights to implement wellness, but you should make it a non-negotiable responsibility.

What is self-care? It is an activity that refreshes, rejuvenates, and replenishes the mind, body, and soul. This could expand activities from a pedicure to boundary-setting with people and workloads. When prioritizing your health in terms of the eight areas of wellness, you will ensure emotional wellness and wholeness.

Self-care has become popular and the talk and attention it gets is absolutely necessary. Self-care is putting an emphasis and making one's mental, physical, and emotional needs a priority.

My favorite phrase that reinforces the need for self-care is, "You can't pour from an empty cup."

Create a self-care plan. List at least one thing you can do to improve your self-care. List the steps you will take and add a due date to hold yourself accountable.

Self-Care Plan:

_____

_____

_____

_____

_____

_____

_____

_____

Action Steps:

_____

_____

_____

_____

_____

_____

Due Date: _____

Mindful Moment

Read the following statement out loud:

I deserve love, happiness, and peace. If I don't believe it now, it's okay. I won't stop working towards the truth of this statement. I am more than what I say I am. I am more than what others think of me. I can exceed my wildest dreams.

Let's evaluate your progress in the eight areas of wellness.

On a scale from 0 to 5, with 0 being not at all and 5 being very much, rate how well you prioritize the following areas:

Emotional—Coping effectively with life and creating satisfying relationships.

0   1   2   3   4   5

Spiritual—Expanding a sense of purpose and meaning in life.

0   1   2   3   4   5

Social—Developing a sense of connection, belonging, and a well-developed support system.

0   1   2   3   4   5

Physical—Recognizing the need for physical activity, healthy foods, and sleep.

0   1   2   3   4   5

Intellectual—Recognizing creative abilities and finding ways to expand knowledge and skills.

0   1   2   3   4   5

Occupational—Personal satisfaction and enrichment from one's work.

0   1   2   3   4   5

Environmental—Good health by occupying pleasant, stimulating environments that support well-being.

0   1   2   3   4   5

Financial—Satisfaction with current and future financial situations.

0   1   2   3   4   5

How do your initial scores and your current scores compare? What thoughts and emotions were triggered by the activity?

_____

_____

_____

_____

_____

_____

_____

_____

_____

_____

_____

_____

_____

_____

_____

_____

_____

_____

_____

_____

_____

_____

_____

_____

_____

_____

How are you doing/progressing with your wellness plan? Update your wellness plan to help you achieve your goal. List at least one thing you can do to improve your current level of functioning. List the steps you'll take and add a due date to hold yourself accountable.

Emotional Wellness Plan:

_____

_____

_____

_____

_____

_____

_____

_____

_____

_____

Action Steps:

_____

_____

_____

_____

_____

_____

Due Date: _____

Spiritual Wellness Plan:

_____

_____

_____

_____

_____

_____

_____

_____

_____

_____

Action Steps:

_____

_____

_____

_____

_____

_____

Due Date: _____

Social Wellness Plan:

_____

_____

_____

_____

_____

_____

_____

_____

_____

_____

Action Steps:

_____

_____

_____

_____

_____

_____

Due Date: _____

Physical Wellness Plan:

_____

_____

_____

_____

_____

_____

_____

_____

_____

_____

_____

Action Steps:

_____

_____

_____

_____

_____

_____

Due Date: _____

Intellectual Wellness Plan:

_____

_____

_____

_____

_____

_____

_____

_____

_____

_____

Action Steps:

_____

_____

_____

_____

_____

_____

Due Date: _____

Occupational Wellness Plan:

_____

_____

_____

_____

_____

_____

_____

_____

_____

_____

Action Steps:

_____

_____

_____

_____

_____

_____

_____

Due Date: _____

Financial Wellness Plan:

_____

_____

_____

_____

_____

_____

_____

_____

_____

_____

Action Steps:

_____

_____

_____

_____

_____

_____

Due Date: _____

Environmental Wellness Plan:

_____

_____

_____

_____

_____

_____

_____

_____

_____

_____

Action Steps:

_____

_____

_____

_____

_____

_____

Due Date: _____

Mindful Moment

Body Scan

1. Set a timer for one minute.

2. Sit up straight or lie flat on the floor.

3. Quiet your mind.

4. Start at the top of your head and focus on relaxing your head.

5. Slowly work your way down, relaxing each part of your body (neck, shoulders, torso, pelvis, legs, and feet).

6. If you finish before the timer, lie still, and relax.

Let's re-evaluate and compare your scores.

On a scale of 0 to 5, with 0 being not at all and 5 being very much, rate how you currently feel in the following categories:

Confident

0   1   2   3   4   5

Happy

0   1   2   3   4   5

Sad

0   1   2   3   4   5

Disgusted

0   1   2   3   4   5

Overwhelmed

0   1   2   3   4   5

Alone

0   1   2   3   4   5

Loved

0   1   2   3   4   5

Liked

0   1   2   3   4   5

Attractive

0   1   2   3   4   5

Depressed

0   1   2   3   4   5

Anxious

0   1   2   3   4   5

Healthy

0   1   2   3   4   5

Satisfied

0   1   2   3   4   5

Fulfilled

0   1   2   3   4   5

How do your initial scores and your current scores compare? What thoughts and emotions were triggered by the activity?

_____

_____

_____

_____

_____

_____

_____

_____

_____

_____

_____

_____

_____

_____

_____

_____

_____

_____

_____

_____

_____

_____

_____

_____

As you continue to progress, repeat each activity and write about your experience and growth on the following note sheets.

Made in the USA
Middletown, DE
23 May 2021